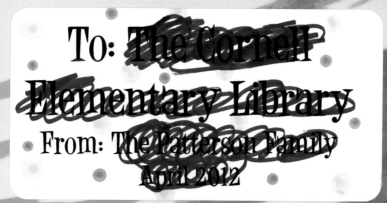

A Clearwater Marine Aquarium **Sea Stars** Story

Winter's Tale

Based on the true story of Winter,
the dolphin who lost her tail

Joanne Benazzi Friedland

Design and Layout by Tracy Kuramoto

Page of Aquarius Press

Chicago, IL

Acknowledgements

The author wishes to thank the following people at Clearwater Marine Aquarium
for making this book possible:
David Yates, Chief Executive Officer,
Diane Young, Director of Animal Care & Stranding Coordinator,
Abby Stone, Head Trainer,
and
Rebecca Bakke-Snowden, Graphic Design/Marketing, for her invaluable assistance.

The author also wishes to thank Tracy Kuramoto for his vision in bringing
Winter's Tale to life with his graphic design, and Kathleen Forde for her thoughtful editing.

Finally, the author wishes to thank Winter for her inspirational spirit.

Chicago, Illinois

Copyright ©2009 Joanne Benazzi Friedland

Published by
Page of Aquarius Press
1424 North State Parkway
Chicago, Illinois 60610

Design and Layout,
Tracy Kuramoto

International Standard Book Number (ISBN) 978-0-9814677-0-2

Printed in Thailand
First Edition, 2009
Second Edition, 2011
Third Edition, 2011

The dolphins in this book are real.

The people in this story are fictional,
but they represent the many dedicated men and women who care for these dolphins.

Clearwater Marine Aquarium in Clearwater, Florida,
is where this story takes place.

It is the home of these dolphins.

Introduction

When the baby was born, no one knew she was going to be special.

She was born knowing how to swim. That would have been pretty special for you or me, but since she was a dolphin, it was normal.

She was born in the sea, but she could not breathe underwater like a fish. Her mother pushed her to the surface so she could take her first breath of salty ocean air through the blowhole on the top of her head. Soon she was able to swim up by herself whenever she needed to take a breath.

She was born knowing that she should swim very close to her mother. This not only kept her safe but was also easier than swimming alone, because her mother's movement through the water created a wave to pull her along.

The calf spent her first weeks with her mother, just as other baby dolphins do.

But when she was only about two months old, something happened to change her from an ordinary dolphin to a very special one indeed.

Curious Kids' Corner

I thought this was a book about a dolphin. Where did the "calf" come from?

A baby dolphin is called a "calf," just like a baby cow you might see on a farm. The word "calf" is also used for a baby camel, giraffe, whale, elephant, rhinoceros, hippopotamus or reindeer.

What kind of dolphin is this story about?

The dolphins in this story are called Atlantic bottlenose dolphins. The "Atlantic" in the name means that this kind of dolphin lives in the Atlantic Ocean. The "bottle-nose" part of the name comes from their long snouts that look a bit like the neck of a bottle.

How does a dolphin breathe?

You can breathe through your nose or your mouth, but a dolphin breathes through the blowhole on top of its head. That is a good place for it, because it lets the dolphin take a breath while swimming without lifting its whole head out of the water.

Is a dolphin a fish?

No, a dolphin is a kind of animal that is called a "mammal." Dogs, cats, mice, horses, cows, lions and elephants are also mammals. So are people!

Birds, fish, lizards, snakes, insects and crabs are not mammals.

What makes a dolphin a mammal?

Mammals have lungs to breathe air. Dolphins need to come up to the surface whenever they need to take a breath. An adult dolphin can swim underwater for five to seven minutes between breaths. How long can you hold your breath?

Mammals give birth to their babies instead of laying eggs. A dolphin mother is pregnant for almost a year before her calf is born. Your mother was pregnant for about nine months before you were born. A baby dolphin weighs about forty-five pounds at birth. How much did you weigh? A newborn baby dolphin is about forty-five inches long. How long were you at birth?

Mammal mothers produce milk to feed their babies.

Mammals also have hair. Baby dolphins are born with a few chin whiskers that soon fall out. Dolphins may also have a tiny bit of hair near their blowholes.

Winter demonstrates how a dolphin baby bends up the sides of her long tongue to make a tube, like a straw, to drink milk from her mother's body while swimming underwater.

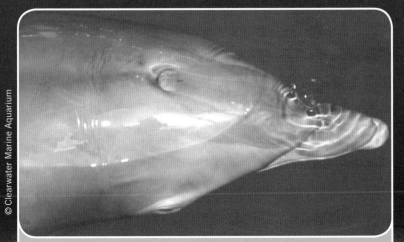

Your nostrils are always open, but since a dolphin spends most of its time underwater, the blowhole is closed when the dolphin relaxes and the dolphin has to use muscles to open it.

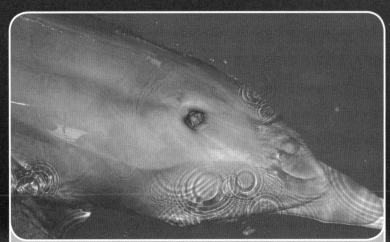

When a dolphin comes up to take a breath, it quickly blows out old air and takes in new air.

Chapter One

It was December, but the bright Florida sunshine warmed the water of the lagoon. Waves kicked up clouds of fine, white sand on the ocean floor. The mother dolphin swam along looking for fish to eat, and her baby followed.

Everything was a toy for the baby dolphin. A fish swimming by was something to chase. A piece of seaweed was something to toss in the air and wrap around her long snout.

Rene Frederick / Digital Vision / Getty Images

As the baby dolphin came to the surface to take a breath, she saw a white ball floating nearby. She left her mother and swam over to take a look. A long rope hung down from the ball and disappeared into the dark sea below. As the waves rocked the ball, the rope danced. This was a wonderful toy!

She grabbed the rope in her teeth and tugged. The end of the rope seemed to be stuck on something. The calf was curious, so she swam downward to follow the rope. Its end was tied to a heavy wire cage sitting on the sandy bottom. There was a blue crab in the cage. He looked a bit angry about being stuck in there, but blue crabs are often grumpy.

While her mother followed a school of fish, the baby dolphin played with her new toy. She took the rope in her mouth and swam in circles, watching the white ball skip along behind her. When she stopped, the rope formed a lazy loop, so she swam through it. She pulled hard on the rope to make the cage tip and the crab complain. Finally, she stopped to rest.

As she swam to the surface and took a breath, she felt the rope pinch her jaw. Ouch! She tried to spit the rope out of her mouth, but it was tangled around her head and fins. One loop of the rope even circled the base of her tail. Suddenly she felt frightened, so she cried out to her mother. She was trapped!

The mother dolphin swam back as fast as she could. She saw that the calf was tangled in the rope of a crab trap, but she could not figure out how to free her. The more the baby dolphin struggled, the tighter the rope became.

Soon the sun was high overhead, and the baby was very uncomfortable. The tingling in her strangled tail had become a throbbing pain. Her mouth was sore from the rough rope, and she was very hungry. She could not close her mouth to swallow because the rope was in the way.

The mother dolphin stayed with her baby all that day and all through that night. Late the next afternoon, the two dolphins heard a sound. The calf did not know what it was, but the mother knew it was the sound of people talking.

The people were walking behind the mangrove trees on the shore. Soon they would be in a clearing where they could see the mother and baby dolphin.

Normally, the mother dolphin would not have wanted people to come close to her calf, but this was an emergency. People had made that crab trap and that rope. Maybe they would know how to set her baby free. The mother made her decision. She swam away from her baby!

The baby was very hungry and tired, but when she saw her mother leaving, she whistled and squeaked as loudly as she could. She used every last bit of strength to call her mother, but the mother did not answer. The mother quietly watched the shore and waited. In a few moments, she saw the people in the clearing. They heard her baby calling and looked out across the water to where the calf was trapped.

The mother hoped the people would help soon. Her baby did not have much time!

11

Curious Kids' Corner

How does a crab trap work?

A crab trap is a cage with special holes that let crabs crawl in but not out again. The person who owns the crab trap puts a piece of fish or other food into the trap as bait, throws the trap into the water, and leaves. If any crabs come by, they will smell the bait and crawl around on the trap until they find the way to get in. The good news for the crabs is that they get to eat some of the bait. The bad news is that the crabs cannot leave after their dinner.

The people who set the crab trap come back the next day, take the trap out of the water and remove the crabs they caught. If they want to, they can put more bait in the trap and throw it back in.

Why are ropes and balls tied to crab traps?

Crab traps are usually set pretty far from the shore, so the people setting the trap use a boat to get to the spot where they will put the trap. Once the trap is thrown into the water, it sinks to the bottom and is hard to find because the water is deep. The rope tied to the trap has a floating ball on the end to show the owners where the trap is. The ball is called a "buoy."

When the owners want to check the trap, they use a long stick with a hook at the end to snag the buoy and rope and pull them onto the boat. Then they use the rope to pull the trap up onto the boat so they can remove the crabs inside.

© Clearwater Marine Aquarium

If you take the Sea Life Safari cruise at Clearwater Marine Aquarium, you will see the crew pull in a crab trap.

Are crab traps bad?

Crab traps do not usually hurt other animals when they are used properly. They have special holes to let fish swim in and out of them. Dolphins, turtles and other animals sometimes get tangled in the ropes of crab traps, but if the owners come back each day, they can set the animals free before they get hurt. The problem is that some owners set their traps and do not check them often enough.

A Clearwater Marine Aquarium volunteer points out the holes that let fish escape from crab traps. The small cage in the center of the trap holds the bait.

Do dolphins talk?

Dolphins do not speak in words as we do, but they make lots of different sounds to communicate with each other. Some of these sounds are like whistles, some are like clicks, some are like grunts, and some even sound like creaky doors.

Each adult bottlenose dolphin makes up its own special pattern of sounds. When the other dolphins in the group hear that pattern, they know which dolphin is communicating.

When a baby dolphin is born, its mother creates a special pattern of sounds that she uses with her baby. She will repeat that pattern over and over again during the baby's first few weeks. The baby learns that pattern and is able to find its mother when they are separated or are in a group with other dolphins.

Chapter Two

Adam did not want to be out in the sunshine on that beautiful December afternoon. He wanted to be in his room playing his new computer game. All of his friends had made it to level five, and they kept talking about it at school. Adam could reach that level too, if only his mom would leave him alone.

Instead, she made him come along for this stupid walk to the beach. He had seen the beach a gazillion times before, and it was never as interesting as his computer games.

He did not like getting sand in his shoes. He did not like walking barefoot and having to watch for sharp shells. He did not like the smell of the icky seaweed that would pile up at the high-tide line.

He kind of liked the pinkish-purple Portuguese man-o-war jellyfish that sometimes washed up on the beach, but he pretended to be bored if his mom was watching. Every single time they saw one, his mom would tell him not to touch it because it could sting him, even after it was dead. Did she think he was going to forget something like that?

A horseshoe crab shed this shell when he was ready to grow larger.

He was thinking about how he would get past the dragon on the drawbridge in his game when they walked out of the mangrove trees and into the clearing. He was trying not to listen to his mom's cheerful chatter about a horseshoe crab shell she had found. Suddenly he heard the weak call of the baby dolphin. His mom heard it too, and they both squinted across the water and saw the trapped calf.

His mom called for help on her cell phone. Soon she was talking to the Stranded Marine Animal Hotline. Adam and his mom waited.

The sun was starting to set. It was time for Adam to start his homework and his mom to start making dinner, but they sat together on the sand. They could see that the baby dolphin was very weak, and they hoped that the rescuers would arrive soon. The boy forgot to look bored. He even let his mom put her arm around his shoulders, and he found that it felt good.

Out of sight under the water, another mother was also watching and worrying.

© Peter and Kathleen Forde

Chapter Three

When the call came in, Brian was packing his briefcase to leave work.

He had been the leader of a marine animal stranding response team for three years. The wetsuit and faded swim trunks he kept in his car, just in case, gave off a low-tide stink that no air freshener could cover. He was used to it, but his girlfriend wouldn't ride in his car.

He drove to Mosquito Lagoon, thinking about all of the animals he had helped. The rest of the stranding team was ready by the time Brian stretched the wetsuit over his shoulders. He swam out to the crab trap with two other divers and carefully freed the baby dolphin from the tangled rope.

He could see that the calf was very frightened. She had probably never even seen people before, and now human hands were holding her and touching the places where she hurt the most. Brian spoke to the other team members very softly. He tried to move smoothly and slowly to avoid startling the calf.

© Clearwater Marine Aquarium

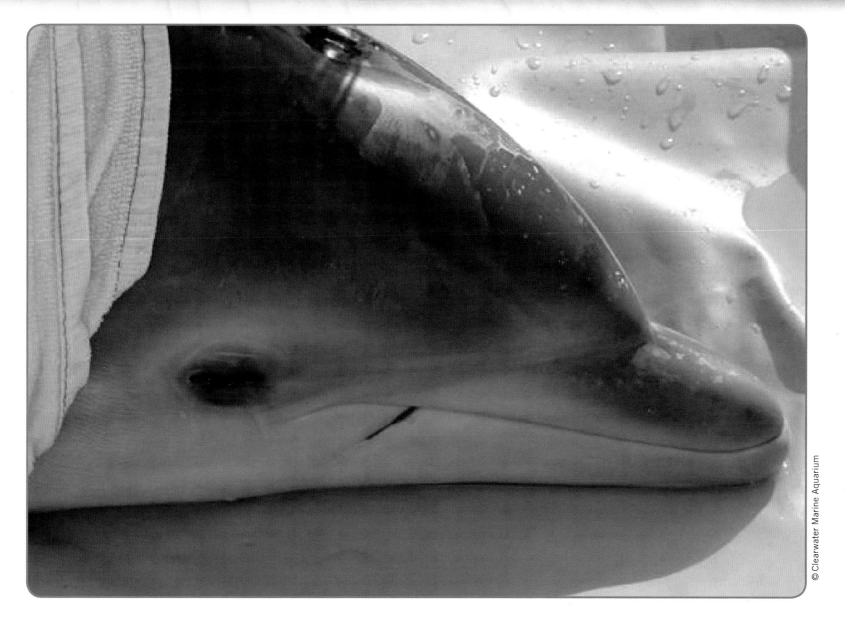

Brian took a moment to examine the baby dolphin. The red sores the rope had made at the corners of her mouth and on her tongue looked painful, but not serious. The wounds on her body and near her fins where the rope had wrapped around her also looked like they would heal soon.

What worried him was her tail. It was limp and a sickly gray color. The tight noose of rope around the base of her tail had cut off the blood supply. Brian had seen many hurt and sick dolphins during his work with the team, but never anything like this.

© Clearwater Marine Aquarium

Brian gave the signal to move the calf to the truck. The team slipped a canvas sling under the calf and lifted her out of the water. She was so much lighter than the other dolphins Brian had helped.

He estimated this calf's age at only two or three months. Brian knew that wild baby dolphins stay with their mothers for two or three years. Could a baby this young and weak survive without her mother?

The baby dolphin tried to break free as she was removed from the water and carried into the stranding team's truck. She began to call for her mother once again, but there was no answer.

Her mother watched until the lights of the truck disappeared and then swam away slowly. If dolphins could cry tears, the sea would have overflowed that night.

CLEARWATER MARINE AQUARIUM

MARINE ANIMAL
STRANDING TEAM
727-441-1790

WWW.CMAquarium.org

I08 JYN

21

Curious Kids' Corner

What should I do if I find a sick or wounded dolphin?

The best thing to do is call for help. Most police, lifeguards and other emergency workers will know how to reach the local marine animal stranding hotline. Do not go near the animal because it may feel threatened and try to bite you.

Sometimes, a sick or injured dolphin gets too weak to swim against the tide so it washes up on the beach and gets stranded. Do not try to push the animal back out into deeper water. It may be unable to swim and could drown.

What kind of animals do marine animal stranding teams help?

Each stranding team is qualified to help the animals in its area. The Clearwater Marine Aquarium stranding team, for instance, helps dolphins, whales, manatees, river otters and sea turtles.

How do stranding teams reach the animal that needs help?

The stranding team has a truck that is like an ambulance for animals. It is specially suited for its work on beaches because it has four-wheel drive and a ramp to help in loading heavy animals. In some cases, the stranding team will also use a boat, kayak or jet ski to reach a sick or injured animal.

© Clearwater Marine Aquarium

A volunteer feeds Cocoa, a green sea turtle. Cocoa came to Clearwater Marine Aquarium after a boat hit her, injuring her skull. The accident left her blind so she now lives at the Clearwater Marine Aquarium.

© Clearwater Marine Aquarium

Bella the baby river otter was found swimming in the pool of the Belleview Biltmore Resort. Her mother was not around and she was too young to be on her own, so she now lives at the Clearwater Marine Aquarium.

How does the stranding team take care of an injured dolphin?

The medical experts on the team check out the animal's injury or sickness while the other helpers try to keep the animal safe and comfortable. You are most comfortable when you are warm and dry, but a healthy dolphin needs to be wet and cool. If the dolphin is stuck on the sand and not completely covered by water, someone will cover it with a wet towel so it will not get sunburned.

© Clearwater Marine Aquarium

Winter needed to wear zinc oxide while recovering from the loss of her tail because she was held at the surface of the water so she could breathe.

Dolphins can get sunburned?

Yes, just like people, dolphins can get sunburned. When a dolphin is swimming in the ocean, the water protects its skin, but if the dolphin is stuck on the sand, its skin can burn very quickly. A stranding team helper will put a special sunscreen (called zinc oxide) on a stranded dolphin's skin to protect it from the sun, just as your mom or dad puts sunscreen on you. If you visit Clearwater Marine Aquarium, look for Nicholas, the dolphin who was badly sunburned when he was stranded.

Since Winter was covered by water while she was stuck in the crab-trap rope, she did not get sunburned. The stranding team put a wet towel over her to protect her skin from sunburn when they removed her from the water.

© Clearwater Marine Aquarium

Nicholas still has scars on his back from his sunburn. He is shown here swimming with Indy.

Chapter Four

The baby dolphin was given the name, "Winter," because she was found in the month of December.

Brian decided that Winter would be taken to Clearwater Marine Aquarium, because the people there had cared for very young dolphins before.

He checked the baby's condition during the long drive. At one point, when he rested his hand near Winter's head, the calf snapped at it but missed. He thought that was a good sign. Even though Winter was weak and sick, she was spunky. Perhaps she would fight to get well.

Brian knew from experience that he would be up for most of the night, helping where he could and watching over the baby dolphin. He would need lots of strong coffee to stay awake at work tomorrow.

It was dark by the time the stranding team arrived at Clearwater Marine Aquarium, but Dr. Clark, the aquarium's veterinarian, and other aquarium workers were waiting. The stranding team used the canvas sling to carry the calf to a large blue pool in the yard behind the aquarium building.

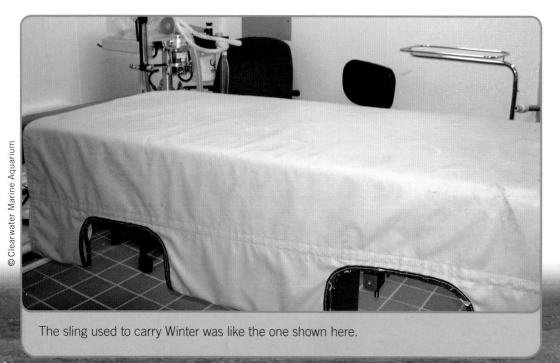

© Clearwater Marine Aquarium

The sling used to carry Winter was like the one shown here.

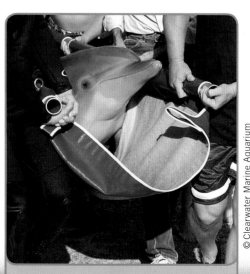

© Clearwater Marine Aquarium

Poles can be slipped through the sides of the sling to make it easier to carry while the animal is gently cradled in the strong canvas.

Dr. Clark climbed into the pool and put her arms around Winter as she was slipped into the water. The calf started to sink because she was too weak to swim, so Dr. Clark gently held her up to keep her blowhole above the water.

Dr. Clark knew that the baby needed food and medicine. She gave the calf a mixture similar to the milk Winter's mother had fed her. Then she cleaned the calf's wounds and applied a soothing ointment.

There was nothing more Dr. Clark could do to help the calf that night, but she was worried. Any dolphin calf of Winter's age who was separated from its mother would probably die, and because of Winter's injuries, her weakness from the long time she spent tangled in the rope, and the fright of being removed from her ocean home and surrounded by people, it seemed that it would take a miracle to save Winter's life.

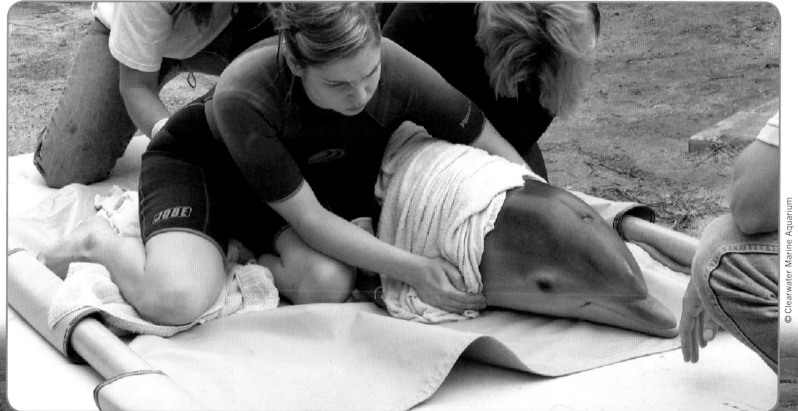

The other people took turns staying in the pool with Winter to keep her blowhole above the surface, but Dr. Clark had to leave. There were important surgeries on sea turtles scheduled for the morning. She had to get a few hours of sleep so she could give them a chance to live as well.

When Dr. Clark arrived at the Aquarium early the next day, the first thing she did was check on little Winter. Winter had survived the night! Maybe she could get better after all.

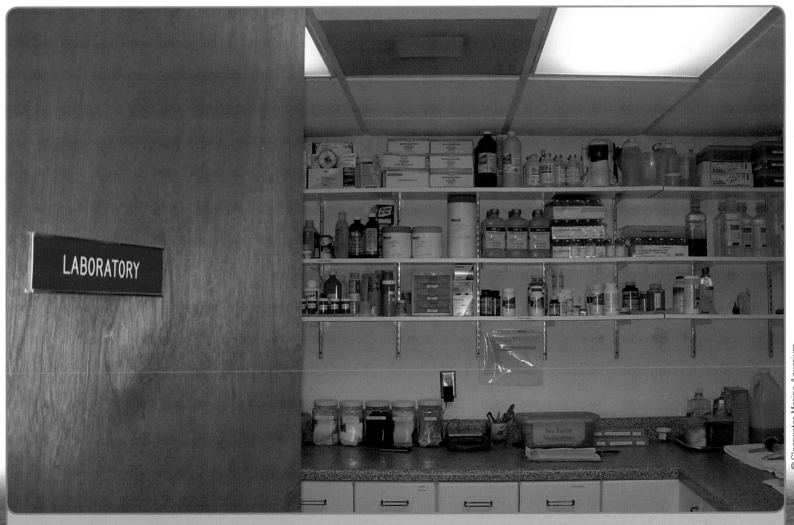

LABORATORY

Clearwater Marine Aquarium keeps a wide variety of medicines on hand to treat injured and sick sea animals.

Chapter Five

The next morning, everything at Clearwater Marine Aquarium seemed the same as usual to all of the visitors. The Sea Life Safari cruise left on time at 11:00 a.m. The dolphin presentation started at noon. Children stuck their hands into the water at "Stingray Beach" to feel the surprisingly silky skin of the rays. There was the normal schedule of presentations to teach visitors about the sea turtles, river otters, dolphins and sharks at the aquarium. But news about Winter's arrival spread quickly among the staff and volunteers.

Denise, the head of the Marine Mammal Department at the aquarium, was in charge of caring for this fragile baby dolphin. Winter needed to have someone with her all day and night, every day and night, because she was so young and so badly hurt. Everyone wanted to help. The staff and volunteers soon taught Winter to drink from a bottle. Every two hours she would slurp down a special mixture of powdered baby animal formula, goat's milk, oil, vitamins and medicine.

Denise made sure Winter's wounds were cleaned and ointment was put on her sore mouth, body, and tail many times each day to help them heal. Even with all that gentle care, Winter's tail did not get better. It was withering up and dead pieces of her tail kept peeling off. By the fifth day after Winter's rescue, her entire tail was gone.

Denise watched Dr. Clark treat the stump where the tail had been and worried about this baby. A dolphin needs its tail to push its body through the water. When Winter's tail fell off, she could no longer swim. How could a dolphin live without a tail?

Winter had weighed seventy-five pounds when she was first rescued. Now, without her tail, she weighed sixty-nine pounds. She continued to lose weight after losing her tail. That was a very bad sign. A baby dolphin needs to grow and get heavier.

By her tenth day at the aquarium, Winter was down to sixty-six pounds. Denise and the other staffers and volunteers caring for Winter were heartbroken to see that she was still losing weight.

But Winter had not given up.

Curious Kids' Corner

What is a dolphin's tail made of?

There are no bones or muscles in a dolphin's tail. The tail is connective tissue covered with skin. If you could touch a dolphin's tail, it would feel like a thick slab of very hard rubber.

How can part of an animal's body die?

We all know that every animal needs air, food and water to live. Each part of its body has to get its share of these things. If any part does not get enough air, food or water for a long time, it will die. After this happens, even with lots of air, water and food, it cannot get better. It takes a very bad injury to make a part of a body die.

© Clearwater Marine Aquarium

Nicholas shows us what a healthy dolphin tail should look like.

Why did the rope cause Winter's tail to die?

Tiny bits of air, food and water are carried to each part of an animal's body by blood. Blood flows through tiny tubes called "blood vessels."

It may help you understand if you think of these blood vessels as tunnels and think of the blood as a train carrying tiny bits of food. If the tunnel collapses, the train cannot get through.

The rope around Winter's tail was so tight that it caused the vessels bringing blood to Winter's tail to collapse, so no blood could get through. The rope stayed on so long that all of Winter's tail died.

Chapter Six

It was 1:00 a.m. on Christmas Day and there were lots of places Ed could have been. He could have been in his cozy bed at home, of course. After all, he had worked a full day and then done some Christmas shopping.

He could have been helping his wife set out milk and cookies for Santa Claus.

Instead, he was walking into Clearwater Marine Aquarium because he had volunteered to help care for Winter. He yawned as he put on his swimsuit. Ed entered the pool from the steps, cleaning his feet in a small tub and splashing as little as possible. He waited until another volunteer moved away from Winter before he walked to the dolphin. Winter had figured out that if there were two people in the pool with her, they probably were going to treat her wound or give her a shot of medicine. Tonight, Ed was just there to help Winter swim and keep her company.

He put his hand under Winter's chin to keep her blowhole above the water and started walking in the pool, slowly leading the baby dolphin. He had not seen Winter for a whole week, so he looked her over, hoping to see some improvement. He was no longer shocked that her graceful shape ended abruptly in the rounded stump where her tail should have been. He was happy to see that the redness had gone away. The stump seemed to be healing.

Denise startled him when she appeared at the door. She had other places she could be too, but she had come to check on Winter one more time. She cared deeply about all of the aquarium's animals, but there was a special place in her heart for Winter.

Denise handed Ed the warm bottle she had prepared for Winter's 1:45 a.m. feeding. It reminded Ed of when his children were babies. Taking care of them had seemed like a big job at the time, but at least he didn't have to climb into a pool in the middle of the night to feed them!

Ed was happy to see how eagerly Winter accepted her bottle and gulped down her formula.

"I think Winter looks better than last week," Ed said. Denise was feeling a little discouraged about Winter, but she looked at the calf again and tried to see the progress Ed saw.

"Let's weigh her after she finishes eating," Denise replied. It was easy for the two of them to lift her from the water onto the scale.

Denise smiled. For the first time since Winter's arrival at the aquarium two weeks earlier, the little dolphin had gained weight! They gently returned Winter to the water.

39

Maybe Winter was finally getting better. The sound of human voices no longer frightened her, but Ed still spoke softly as he guided Winter through the water. Suddenly, Ed's feet slipped, and his head went under the surface. Without meaning to, he reached for the side of the pool and let go of Winter's chin. When he got back onto his feet and shook the water from his eyes, he saw something amazing: Winter was swimming without his help!

Without a tail, she could not swim like a dolphin, but she had taught herself to swim like a fish, moving her tail stump from side to side. Denise and Ed stood in shocked silence for a moment and then started laughing in voices that were a little too loud. Winter did not seem to mind.

Ed reached out his hand to support Winter's chin, but she shook her head from side to side as if she were saying, "No." She wanted to swim on her own. Denise and Ed were thrilled and let her go. After a short swim, she got tired and came back to Ed. He held up her chin and let her rest for awhile, but then she shook off his hand to swim by herself again. Ed's two-hour shift flew by.

When the next volunteer arrived to take over Winter's care, Ed didn't want to leave, but he knew that his kids would be waking up in a few hours, and he needed to get some sleep before the Christmas chaos began. As he walked to his car, he hummed a Christmas carol, and the Florida moon smiled down on him.

41

Curious Kids' Corner

How fast can bottlenose dolphins swim?

Generally they swim three to seven miles per hour, but when they need a burst of speed to catch some dinner or to escape from danger, they can swim about twenty to twenty-five miles per hour. The fastest people can swim about five miles per hour.

How do dolphins swim?

As you know dolphins are mammals, like whales, otters, seals and people. All mammals swim in pretty much the same way. People kick their feet up and down. Dolphins, whales and other sea mammals move their tails up and down to swim.

People also use their hands and arms to swim, but a dolphin's tail is so strong that it does not need to use its side flippers to propel itself. Dolphin side flippers, called "pectoral fins," are used, like the rudder of a boat, for steering and stopping.

Have you ever tried to swim with flippers on your feet? They make your kicking powerful enough that you do not need to use your arms. Next time you have some flippers, try swimming like a dolphin!

How did Winter swim without her tail?

Winter taught herself to swim in a totally new way. She moved her body from side to side. Fish swim that way, but they usually have vertical tails to give them a push. Since Winter did not have a vertical tail, she had to use her pectoral fins to get herself started, just as we use our arms to swim.

Was it hard for Winter to swim this new way?

Winter's body is not that different from yours, so you can answer this question yourself. Lie on your bed on your stomach, and make believe that your ankles are tied together. Bend your knees to move your feet up off the bed and back down. This is a bit like how a dolphin usually swims. Is it hard to do? Do you think you could do that over and over for a long time?

Now, still on your stomach, again pretend that your ankles are tied together. Keep your feet on the bed, but try to swish them from one side of your bed to the other like a fish. Is that harder? Do you think you would get tired if you had to do this a lot of times? This is like the way Winter swims without her tail.

So now you can tell me: was it hard for Winter to swim this new way?

Just for fun, Winter sometimes swims upside-down. Can you swim on your back?

Chapter Seven

Winter got a little better every day through January, February and March. Her wounds healed, and soon she was eating, playing and growing almost like a normal baby dolphin. She still needed someone with her in the pool all day and night, but she enjoyed playing with her caretakers.

Winter worked with her trainers six or seven times each day. She learned to come to them when they blew their whistles or patted the water. She learned that when a trainer held out her hand, she wanted Winter to touch it with her chin.

© Clearwater Marine Aquarium

Winter learned to wait patiently as the trainers and veterinarians handled her body and gave her medical treatment. She even learned to stay very still with her head straight down and her tail stump straight up so the trainers and veterinarians could check it. The trainers made it a game so she liked to stand on her head!

They never punished Winter for doing something wrong, but they blew a whistle and rewarded her when she did something right. Winter's favorite reward was a back rub or belly rub. She also liked it when the trainers swam with her.

Winter now weighed eighty pounds, but the formula Winter was drinking was not as rich as her mother's dolphin milk would have been. The volunteers now added ground-up fish to Winter's bottles. They held their noses as the blender whirled the herring to make a smelly smoothie but Winter found it delicious.

Soon it was time for Winter to give up her bottles and start eating real fish of different kinds. In the wild, a baby dolphin sees her mother hunting for fish and figures out that fish are food. At the aquarium, the staff and volunteers had to teach Winter to eat fish.

Denise tried putting very small fish into the calf's bottle, so Winter could suck in some whole fish along with her herring milkshake. The first few times they tried this, Winter just spit the fish out.

Denise also tried to teach Winter to hold her mouth open so the trainers could place fish into it. Of course, just because a fish was placed in her mouth did not mean that it would stay there. The first time Winter discovered a fish in her mouth, she spit it right back at the trainer! This became one of Winter's favorite games. The trainers tried not to laugh as they dodged the slimy fish.

After months of patience (and ducking) on the part of her trainers, Winter finally got the idea and learned to eat fish. Denise breathed a sigh of relief. Winter had taken another big step toward normal dolphin life.

Denise knew that Winter could never be released to be a wild dolphin. Even though she could swim, she could not swim as fast as other dolphins, so it would be hard for her to catch fish to eat. Since she had not had much time with her mother, she had not learned the other things a dolphin must know to survive in the ocean.

Winter was now a happy and healthy young dolphin, but Denise knew Winter missed having other dolphins to keep her company. Denise decided to help Winter with that problem.

What do dolphins eat?

Dolphins eat a wide variety of fishes, squid, crabs and shrimp. The dolphins at Clearwater Marine Aquarium are fed fish of the same quality that you would eat in a fine restaurant!

VITAMINS	VIT E 400 IU	VIT C 500 MG	B 100 COMPLEX	PET CALS	BLUE SEA TAB	ACIDOPHILUS
Panama						
Nicholas						
Indy						

DOLPHINS	Herring	Capelin	Squid	Sardines	Total	• New Protocol for rinsing dolphin food •
Panama	5.5 lbs	9.5 lbs	N/A	2 indv	15.0 lbs	Gently rub herring & capelin to reduce slime layer & to help thaw frozen fish. "Stir" cooler contents each time you rinse. Rinse until water is clear.
Nicholas	7.5 lbs	3 lbs	N/A	2 indv	10.5 lbs	
Indy	7.5 lb	3 lbs	N/A	2 indv	10.5 lbs	as of 1-23-08
Winter	3.0 lbs	7.5 lbs	N/A	2 indv	10.5 lbs.	Coolers should be rinsed 3-5 times

W Diet Change

OTTERS	CAPELIN	LAKESMELT	Herring	Feline Diet	CARROTS	ANTIOXIDANT	DERM CAP	COMMENTS
Webster	0.5 lb	0.25 lb	0.25 lb	0.25 lb	3	Daily	Daily	
Garth	0.5 lb	0.25 lb	0.25 lb	0.25 lb	3	Daily	Daily	
Cooper	1.0 lb	0.5 lb	—	0.25 lb	3	Daily	Daily	
Bogey	1.0 lb	.25 lb	.25 lb		cut in half			
Bella	0.5 lb	0.5 lb	0.5 lb	0.25 lb	3	Daily	Daily	

* Please rinse Lakesmelt

MEDS

Webster
3 AM Capelin
P.M. 2 1/3 glucosamine, 1 derm cap
P.M. 3 3 mazuri
1 PM Capelin

Garth
3 am Capelin
a.m. 1 1/3 glucosamine, 1 derm cap, 2 2.5 cc Orudis, 1 chiang Huo
P.M. 3 3 mazuri, 2.5 cc Orudis
1 PM Capelin

Cooper
* place prednisone in separate meat ball from other meds
4 PM Capelin
a.m. 1 1/3 glucosamine, 1 derm cap, 2 2.5 cc Orudis, 1 chiang Huo, 3/4 Prednisone every other day
P.M. 2.5 cc Orudis
3 3 mazuri, 1 derm cap

Bella
2 AM Capelin
A.M. 2 1 derm cap
3 3 mazuri

Bogey
6 am Capelin (~0.25 lb)
2 mazuri

This bulletin board in the kitchen of Clearwater Marine Aquarium tells the volunteers what food to prepare for each animal at the aquarium.

Do dolphins have teeth?

Adult bottlenose dolphins have about one hundred sharp teeth that are used to catch fish, but not to chew them. They swallow fish whole and head-first so that the spines on the back of the fish do not catch in their throats. Dolphins will sometimes break up fish that are too big to swallow by shaking or rubbing them on the ocean floor.

© Clearwater Marine Aquarium

How do wild dolphins catch fish?

Bottlenose dolphins are very smart and they sometimes work together to catch fish. They have lots of clever ways to hunt for their food. For example, if a group of dolphins sees a large school of fish, they may swim in circles around it so that the fish get very close together. The dolphins then take turns swimming through to eat some of the fish.

Some dolphins may herd a school of fish toward other dolphins, or into shallow water where they are easier to catch. A dolphin may hit a fish with its big strong tail to stun it, making it easier to catch. Dolphins can even blow a cloud of bubbles to confuse fish.

How do dolphins find fish to eat?

Dolphins use echoes to find fish. Have you ever yelled in a tunnel and listened to the echo? The echo is actually the sound you made hitting the wall of the tunnel and bouncing back to your ears. Dolphins make noises in the water and listen to the way the sounds bounce back to them. They can tell when the sounds are bouncing off a school of fish and use the echoes to find them.

How well can dolphins hear?

Dolphins can hear better than people can. They are also much better at figuring out where sounds come from. They use hearing more than eyesight because the water they live in can be murky or dark.

Do dolphins have ears?

A dolphin's ears do not stick out from its head like ours do. Their outer ears are just tiny openings behind their eyes. You can see one of Winter's ears in the picture on the next page.

The inner parts of a dolphin's ear collect sound that comes in through its ear holes. A dolphin also detects sound through its lower jaw which is close to its inner ear. Its lower jaw is filled with a kind of dolphin fat that conducts sound very well.

You can also hear sound that does not come in through your ears. Try this: Press your hands tightly over your ears so no sound can get in. Now, say your name aloud. You can hear your own voice because your head and throat are conducting the sound to your inner ear.

Is Winter smiling for the camera in these pictures?

Bottlenose dolphins look like they are smiling all the time, but that is just the way their mouths are shaped. The people who spend a lot of time caring for and training Winter can tell how she is feeling from the sounds she makes, the way her eyes look, and the way she holds and moves her body, but not from her smile.

Chapter Eight

Panama shows us her worn-down front teeth.

Four years before Winter was born, another dolphin came to live at Clearwater Marine Aquarium. This other dolphin was found near Panama City, Florida, so she was named, "Panama." She was about thirty years old at the time and that is pretty old for a dolphin.

Her front teeth were worn down from her many years in the ocean, so she couldn't catch fish anymore. She became too skinny and got sick, so Panama was given a home at Clearwater Marine Aquarium and soon she was healthy again.

At the aquarium, Panama liked to show off how high she could jump during the dolphin shows. She also liked to play with the aquarium's other dolphins, Nicholas and Indy. But now, Panama had an important job to do.

Panama was not happy to be lifted out of the dolphin pool on the second floor of the aquarium and brought to the special pool where Winter lived. Winter's pool was shaped like a soup bowl, deeper in the center than around the sides. The staff took some water out of the pool so it was too shallow around the edges for Panama to be comfortable. When Panama and Winter were in the pool together, they could see each other and Winter could approach Panama, but Winter could also escape to the shallow water if Panama was too rough. After all, Panama was much bigger, stronger and faster than Winter, and the staff did not want Winter to get hurt.

At first, Winter tried to hide in the shallow water between the pool ladder and the wall, and Panama stayed as far away as she could get.

Winter was afraid of Panama, but she was also very curious and lonely. She had not seen another dolphin for the six months she had been at the aquarium. Winter finally built up the courage to leave her hiding place and swim out into the middle of the pool toward Panama.

Panama was not in a friendly mood. She was cranky about being away from Nicholas and Indy, and she saw that Winter was not a normal dolphin. She had no tail and she did not swim like a dolphin.

Thwack! Panama used her big tail to slap the surface of the water, warning Winter to stay away. Winter darted back to the safety of her hiding place under the ladder.

Indy shows how a dolphin can splash by hitting the surface of the water with his tail.

For three days, Winter kept trying to make friends, and Panama kept turning Winter away. But just as Winter had won the hearts of all the people at Clearwater Marine Aquarium, she finally won the heart of Panama. On the fourth day, Panama let Winter swim into the center of the pool. Soon they were swimming together and then playing together!

Winter once more had a mother.

Curious Kids' Corner

How long do dolphins live?

Most wild bottlenose dolphins live about twenty years, but some can live to be fifty years old.

How big do bottlenose dolphins get?

An adult dolphin will grow to about ten feet long and will weigh four hundred to six hundred pounds. People are generally less than seven feet tall. How tall are you?

Do dolphins live alone or in groups?

Dolphins like living in groups of different sizes, just as people like to live in families. In the area where Winter was found, the average group size is around seven dolphins. How many people live in your home with you?

Just as Winter has Panama to keep her company, Nicholas and Indy, two male Atlantic bottlenose dolphins, share a pool at Clearwater Marine Aquarium.

© Clearwater Marine Aquarium

The trainer looks taller than Indy in this photo, but Indy is still growing and the trainer is cheating by standing on tip toe! Actually, this is the trainer's signal that she wants Indy to balance on his tail.

© Clearwater Marine Aquarium

How high can a dolphin jump?

People have seen wild dolphins jump about sixteen feet in the air and land on their backs or sides. This kind of jump is called a "breach." Experts are not sure why they do this, but it looks like fun!

© Clearwater Marine Aquarium

59

Chapter Nine

© Clearwater Marine Aquarium

Dr. Clark was worried that the "fishy" way Winter swam would hurt her spine over time. The veterinarian could see that Winter often kept her body bent into a shape like the letter "C", and she had never seen another dolphin do that. She wished that Winter could swim like a dolphin again, but to do that, Winter needed a dolphin tail.

There are no stores that sell artificial dolphin tails, so if Winter were to get a new tail, someone would have to invent one for her. Fortunately, that "someone" found his way to Winter.

A man who invents artificial legs for people heard about Winter and decided to help her. It was especially hard to invent an artificial tail for Winter because she had lost both her tail and part of her peduncle. The "peduncle" is the part of the dolphin's body leading to its tail flukes. This section of the body is very muscular and moves the dolphin's tail flukes up and down to swim. The artificial tail would have to be able to move up and down without falling off.

The inventor also had to figure out how to attach the tail to Winter's body. The best answer the inventor found was to make a sleeve to fit over Winter's tail stump. It had to be tight enough to stay on in the water while Winter was swimming and yet not so tight that it would hurt. The inventor made the sleeve out of a type of plastic that is soft but strong. The dolphin trainers then had to teach Winter how to use her new artificial tail.

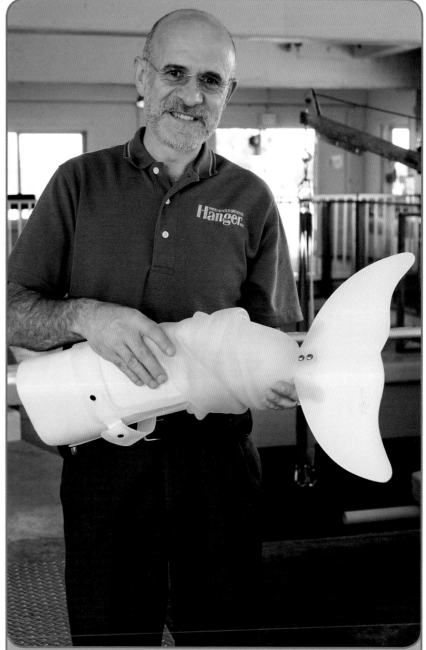

Kevin Carroll holds one of the early versions of Winter's artificial tail. He is the Vice President of Prosthetics of Hanger Orthopedic Group, Inc., the company that is designing and making the tails. All prosthetic services for Winter have been donated by this company. Mr. Carroll has also designed artificial limbs for dogs, and even an ostrich and a duck!

Denise had worked with Winter ever since the calf had come to Clearwater Marine Aquarium, and she knew how to make training sessions fun for Winter. She was very patient and kept the training sessions short and interesting so Winter would not get bored. Denise knew that she could not force Winter to learn if the little dolphin did not want to.

First Denise just showed the artificial tail to her. If Winter looked at it, she was given a reward. The reward was sometimes a favorite food, but more often it was a body rub or a special play period.

After a few weeks, Winter got used to looking at the tail, so Denise started rewarding her if she swam toward the tail. This took a few more weeks. Denise then had to get Winter used to feeling the tail against her skin. Denise would touch different parts of Winter's body with the tail and then give Winter a soothing rubdown.

Many more weeks passed before Denise actually put the tail onto Winter's stump. The first time, Denise rolled up the artificial tail's sleeve and put it just on the very tip of Winter's tail stump. Winter was surprised, but she did not pull away. She had learned to trust Denise. Denise quickly removed the tail and let Winter take the water hose in her mouth and use it to splash her. The hose was one of Winter's favorite toys.

Once Winter was used to having the sleeve on the end of her stump, Denise rolled down a little more of the sleeve and pulled it over a bit more of the tail stump. When Winter was comfortable with that, Denise slipped the whole sleeve over Winter's stump. She then quickly pulled it off, gave Winter lots of praise, and jumped into the pool to swim with Winter. Winter loved it when Denise did that.

Denise worked with Winter to stretch and build up the muscles she would need to swim like a dolphin again. Winter had taught herself to use her side fins to get started when she was swimming without a

©Carol Grant / www.Oceangrant.com

tail. Normal dolphins do not need to do this because their big flat tails are very strong. When Winter was learning to swim with her artificial tail, she kept using her side fins instead of her tail muscles.

Denise came up with a great idea. She knew that Winter loved to be rolled up in the floating water mattress the trainers sometimes put in her pool. When she was rolled up like that, she could not use her side fins. So Denise rolled Winter in the water mattress during her training session with the artificial tail! This made Winter exercise her tail muscles to swim, but for Winter it was just another wonderful game.

After a year of careful training, Winter learned to wear the artificial tail during her training sessions each day and was now able to swim like a dolphin once again.

The bubbles in the water show that Winter is moving her artificial tail up and down to swim.

Winter looks proud of herself, doesn't she?

Chapter Ten

Denise was especially excited one day when she was told that some important people were coming to watch Winter work with her new tail!

Denise smiled at the lovely dolphin Winter had become. She now weighed 185 pounds and was two years old. She was strong and healthy.

The special guests arrived and began to gather around Winter's pool. Denise opened the gate and let them go right up near the edge of the water.

There was the little girl who had an artificial leg. She did not like it when strangers looked at her because she felt different and clumsy. She saw how special Winter was for overcoming problems and learning to use the artificial tail. The little girl now felt that she too was special. She decided to come to the aquarium to see Winter as often as she could, and Winter always seemed happy to see her.

There was a soldier whose leg had been injured so badly that the doctors had removed part of it. She was just getting used to wearing a sleeve like Winter's on her leg. The work the inventor had done on Winter's sleeve had helped his company create a more comfortable sleeve for the soldier.

There was a little boy who had been born with only one leg. He now walked with an artificial leg, but he did not like to do the exercises his doctor wanted him to do because they were boring and they hurt a little. He watched as Denise helped Winter do her dolphin exercises. During the hardest one, Winter glanced at his artificial leg and then looked him right in the eye. The boy decided to try a bit harder at his next exercise session.

Winter seemed to understand that these people were like her, and the people felt it too.

After so many people had helped Winter, it seemed that she now wanted to help people. Winter showed off the things she had learned from the trainers. She loved the attention of all of these visitors and enjoyed hearing them clap for her.

Other guests were also there to watch Winter that morning. Of course, Denise and Dr. Clark were there. They had cared for Winter ever since she first arrived at Clearwater Marine Aquarium. Ed took a day off from work to be there and thought back to that Christmas Day so long ago when Winter taught herself to swim like a fish. Brian and his stranding team came to see how the little dolphin they had rescued had grown. Adam was there and his entire class had come too. Even the bigger kids at school now knew Adam was the kid who had saved Winter, and that was way cooler than beating a computer game.

And miles away, two fishermen felt the cool spray when a dolphin joyfully leapt high into the air near their boat. Did this dolphin mother somehow know that her calf was safe and happy in her new home?

Conclusion

This story is not over, and we do not know how it is going to end.

The inventor is still working on ways to make Winter's tail fit better and work better. Winter will have to continue her exercises and training as she gets used to swimming with the artificial tail. Winter is still a youngster. As she grows, she will need larger tails, and she will have to adapt to each new one.

But there are some parts of the ending that we do know. We know that the people at Clearwater Marine Aquarium will give Winter all the patient, loving care she needs. We also know that Winter will keep trying because she is a little dolphin who does not give up!

About Clearwater Marine Aquarium

Clearwater Marine Aquarium rescues marine animals that are sick or injured and gives them medical care and a safe place to stay while they are recovering. Its stranding response team is one of the nation's most successful teams.

© Clearwater Marine Aquarium

Skylar, a loggerhead turtle, was returned to the sea after being treated at Clearwater Marine Aquarium for six months and cured of her illness.

Whenever possible, rescued animals are released back into the wild. If the experts decide that the animal would not have the strength, skills or physical attributes needed to survive in the wild after it has recovered, the animal is welcomed as a permanent resident of the aquarium.

These permanent residents, including dolphins, sea turtles and river otters, form the core of the aquarium's work to educate children and adults about environmental issues.

© Clearwater Marine Aquarium

© Clearwater Marine Aquarium

Nicholas and Indy like to display their jumping skills during the daily dolphin shows.

Help us take care of Winter and her friends!

Clearwater Marine Aquarium depends upon financial support from the public to pay for veterinary care, food and a healthy, stimulating environment for its resident animals and rescued animals.

Come visit Winter!

Some of this financial support comes from visitors who buy entrance tickets, special tours and items in our gift shop. Please visit our website, **SeeWinter.com**, for help planning your next visit to Clearwater Marine Aquarium.

© Clearwater Marine Aquarium

Visitors to Clearwater Marine Aquarium enjoy educational and entertaining films and presentations about marine animals.

Make a contribution!

People who learn about Winter often wish to help her. One great way is to make a contribution to Clearwater Marine Aquarium. Our website, **SeeWinter.com**, has information about how you can make a donation to help us take care of Winter and her friends.

The Clearwater Marine Aquarium, Inc., is a Florida non-profit organization, which has tax-exempt status under IRC § 501(c)(3). The Aquarium is dedicated to public education, research, animal-assisted therapy and the rescue, rehabilitation and release of sick or injured animals. Donations to the Aquarium may be tax deductible.

Free Guide for Classroom Teachers and Home School Educators

Download your free Educators' Guide to this book at:
www.PageOfAquariusPress.com/WTGuide

In addition to the science taught by this book, the Guide points out the social values illustrated, such as Overcoming Obstacles, Persistence, Patience and Courage.

The Guide includes:

- Motivational Pre-Reading Activities
- Discussion ideas for the themes in Winter's Tale
- Subject-Related Activities for Science, Language Arts, Communications, Computer Skills, Social Studies, Mathematics, Career Education, Art, Music and Vocabulary

This Guide was prepared by Kathleen Forde, a professional educator and department chair with 27 years' experience in one of the finest districts of the New York State Public School system.

Her achievements include:

- NY State English Teacher of Excellence
- National School of Excellence
- Who's Who among American Educators
- Scholastic Magazine Writing Award Honor for Teachers